Tom is playing with his football on the grass.

Dot comes to play. She runs to get the ball.

Dot grabs the ball. Oh no!

Dot pops the football.

Tom is cross. He tells Dot to go away.

Tom gets his bat. He hits
the swingball. Wham!

Dash comes to play. He runs to get the ball.

Tom misses the ball. Dash
grabs the ball.

Oh no! Dash's teeth are stuck in the ball!